Sing to the Moon

The Dragon Kite

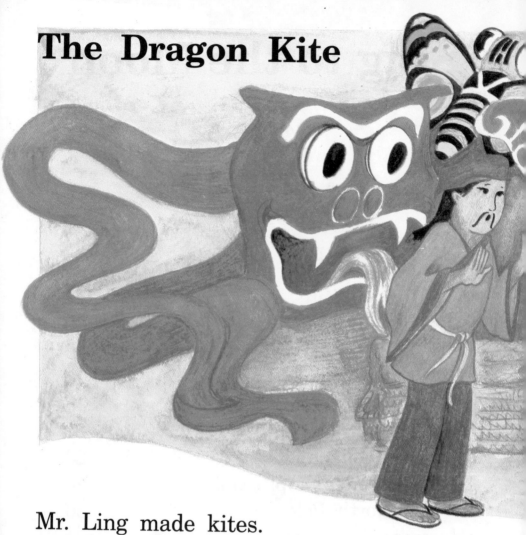

Mr. Ling made kites.
He made kites like birds
and kites like fish.
And he made a dragon kite.

Susan Wu went to Mr. Ling.
"Can I have that dragon kite?" she said.

2

"No," said Mr. Ling.
"Not the dragon kite.
It's too ferocious.
Have a fish kite
or a bird kite."

Susan Wu looked at the dragon kite.
"That's the one I want," she said.
And she pulled it down.

"Don't!" yelled Mr. Ling.

3

The dragon kite laughed a ferocious
laugh and jumped into the sky.
Susan Wu went with it.
"Yippee!" yelled Susan Wu.

"Come back! Come back!
He'll toss you off!" yelled Mr. Ling.

But the dragon kite
and Susan Wu went on,
faster and faster.

"Yippee!" yelled Susan Wu,
over trees and houses.

The dragon kite looked at her.
It laughed its ferocious laugh.
It puffed out fire.

Then it climbed all the way up a rainbow.

It went up and up to the stars.

"Yippee!" yelled Susan Wu.

In and out of the stars they went,
and over the moon.

On the way down, the dragon kite
kicked holes in the clouds.
It splashed the rain about with its tail.

"Don't do that," yelled Susan Wu.
"You'll put your fire out."

The dragon kite looked at Susan Wu and laughed. Susan Wu laughed back.

They came down by Mr. Ling.

"I told you it was a ferocious kite," said Mr. Ling.

"That's all right, Mr. Ling," said Susan Wu. "I'm a ferocious girl."

No Time to Talk

I met a man in the middle of town.
He had his hat on upside down.
I stopped him and I said, "Good day!
Why do you wear your hat that way?"
"Sorry," he said. "No time to talk.
I'm taking my tadpoles for a walk."

The Trader from Currumbin
a play

Father
Mother
Trader
Girl
Boy

● **Trader:**

Knock-knock. Knock.

● **Father:**

One knock twice, and one knock more.
Who's that knocking at our door?

Trader:

I am the trader
from Currumbin.
Open the door
and let me in.
I have hammers
and saws to sell.

Father:

No, no, Trader. Go away.
We don't need hammers
and saws today.

Trader:

Knock-knock. Knock.

Mother:

One knock twice, and one knock more.
Who's that knocking at our door?

11

- **Trader:**

  I am the trader from Currumbin.
  Open the door and let me in.
  I have pots and pans to sell.

- **Mother:**

  No, no, Trader. Go away.
  We don't need pots and pans today.

- **Trader:**

  Knock-knock. Knock.

- **Boy:**

  One knock twice,
  and one knock more.
  Who's that knocking
  at our door?

Trader:

I am the trader from Currumbin.
Open the door and let me in.
I have socks and boots to sell.

Boy:

No, no, Trader. Go away.
We don't need socks and boots today.

Trader:

Knock-knock. Knock.

Girl:

One knock twice,
and one knock more.
Who's that knocking
at our door?

●Trader:

I am the trader from Currumbin.
Open the door and let me in.
I have a bag of stories to tell.

●Girl:

Stories to tell? Why didn't you say?

●Boy:

Come in, come in. Don't go away.

●Father:

We don't need
hammers and saws today.

14

Mother:
We don't need pots and pans today.

Boy:
We don't need socks and boots today.

Girl:
But we *do* need stories.

All:
Every day.

Lawn Mower Poem

Lawn mower, lawn mower,
Snap, snap, snap!
Cutting the grass
In the lawn's green lap.

As I mow up
And down again,
My feet get covered
By a soft, green rain.

16

Every Saturday
I clip and mow
And leave green footprints
Wherever I go.

Through the kitchen,
Up the stair—
Green grass footprints
Everywhere.

The Lawn

"Ah-ha! Rain!"
said the lawn.
"Now I will grow and grow."

"Stop! Stop!" cried the flowers.
"No room! No room!"

"I won't stop," said the lawn.
And it grew and grew.

"Stop! Stop!" cried the lettuce.
"No room! No room!"

"I won't stop," said the lawn.
"I'll grow over the flowers
and over the lettuce.
I'll grow over the garden
and over the town.
I'll be the biggest lawn
in the world."

Then...
snippetty, snappitty,
snippetty, snappitty.
"What's that?" cried the lawn.

"It's Jenny and the lawn mower!"
cried the flowers.

"Hooray! Hooray!
It's lawn mowing day!"
cried the lettuce.

Snippetty, snappitty,
snippetty, snappitty,
went the lawn mower.

"Stop! Stop!"
cried the lawn.

On went Jenny and the lawn mower.
Snippetty, snappitty,
snippetty, snappitty.

The grass got shorter and shorter.

"Just you wait!" grumbled the lawn.
"It will rain again soon."

Ah-ah-*choo!*

Little black beetle,
Sitting on a rose,
Fell on the postman
And tickled his nose.

"Oops!" said the beetle,
"Excuse me, please."
"Oops!" said the postman,
"I'm going to sneeze.
Ah-ah-*choo!*"

22

Come for Lunch

"Please come for lunch,"
Said little Tom Cat.
"What's to eat?" said I.
"Well-cooked mouse
And tail of rat."
"No thanks, Cat," said I.

Red! Green! Stop! Go!

The traffic light was green.
Brrrrrm! went the cars.
Brrrrrrrrm! went the trucks.
BRRRRRRRRRRRM!
went the motor bikes.

"Noise, noise, noise,"
grumbled the traffic light.
"All I get is noise.
I'll make it stop.   I'll turn red."

The traffic light turned red.
The traffic stopped.
The noise stopped.

"Ah, that's lovely,"
said the traffic light.
"Everything is quiet now.
Everything is still.
I'll have a little sleep."

Toot-toot!
One car tooted its horn.
Tooooooooot!
Another car tooted its horn.
Too-oo-oo-oo-ooot!
went the trucks.
Toot-toot-toot!
went the motor bikes.

26

"Stop it! Stop that noise!"
yelled the traffic light.

But the traffic went on tooting.

27

we're late
we're late

"I don't like this tooting
and hooting," grumbled
the traffic light.
"I'll have to turn green."

Brrrrrm!
Off went the cars.
Brrrrrrrrrm!
Off went the trucks.
BRRRRRRRRRRRM!
Off went the motor bikes.

"That's a lot better than
tooting and hooting,"
said the traffic light.
"Traffic noise is not so bad
after all."

At the North Pole

To say while you bounce a ball.

Hello, hello, hello, sir.
Meet you at the corner, sir.
Can't, sir.
Why, sir?
Got a bad cold, sir.
Where did you get the cold, sir?
At the North Pole, sir.
What were you doing there, sir?
Catching polar bears, sir.
How many did you catch, sir?
One, sir, two, sir, three, sir...

30

Hammer, Hammer, Hammer

Danny was making a spaceship.
Hammer, hammer, hammer.

"Look out for that
hammer," said Dad.
"Don't hit your thumb."

"I won't," said Danny.
But he *did* hit his thumb.
The hammer came down
on it.   Whack!

"Ow!" yelled Danny.
Then he cried.

Danny ran to Dad.
"Put your thumb
under the faucet," said Dad.
"Cold water will make it better."

Danny put his thumb
in the cold water.
"It's not getting better," he said.

32

"Let's put a bandage on it,"
said Dad. He got a bandage
and put it around the thumb.
"Is it better now?" he asked.

"No!" said Danny,
and he went on crying.

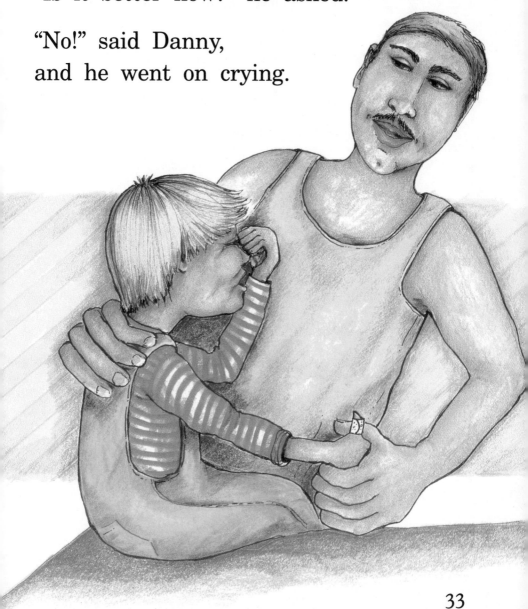

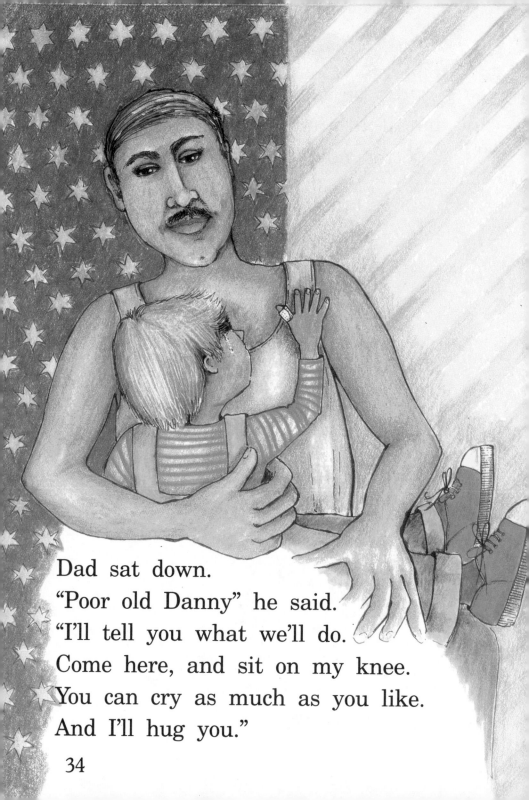

Dad sat down.
"Poor old Danny" he said.
"I'll tell you what we'll do.
Come here, and sit on my knee.
You can cry as much as you like.
And I'll hug you."

34

So Danny got on Dad's knee.
He cried and cried and cried.
Dad hugged him and sang a song.
The song was about a boy
who hit his thumb with a hammer.

Then Danny got down.
"Thanks, Dad," he said.
"My thumb's better now."

"Where are you going?" asked Dad.

"Out to make my spaceship,"
said Danny.

"That's good," said Dad.
"But look out for that
hammer."

35

Whoops!

A horse and a flea
And three blind mice
Sat on a tree stump
Eating rice.

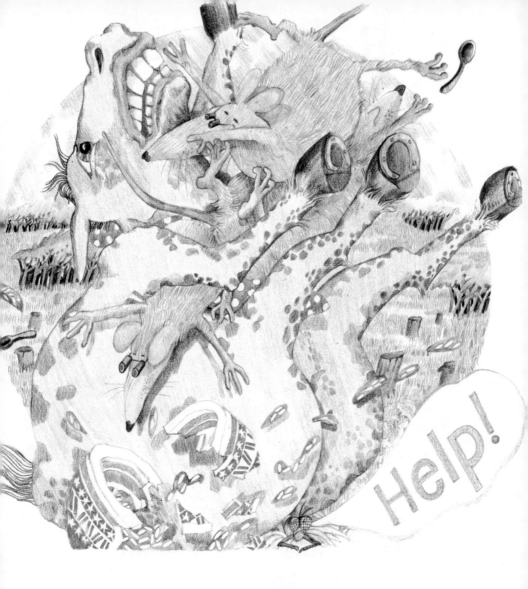

The horsey slipped
And fell on the flea.
"Whoops!" said the flea,
"There's a horse on me."

Roo-roo-roo

Sing to the tune of
"There Were Three Jolly Fishermen."

I got kicked by a kangaroo.
I got kicked by a kangaroo.
Kanga, kanga,
Roo-roo-roo.
Kanga, kanga,
Roo-roo-roo.
I got kicked by a kangaroo.

I got bitten by a bandicoot.
I got bitten by a bandicoot.
  Bandi, bandi,
  Coot-coot-coot.
  Bandi, bandi,
  Coot-coot-coot.
I got bitten by a bandicoot.

I got pushed by a platypus.
I got pushed by a platypus.
  Platy, platy,
  Pus-pus-pus.
  Platy, platy,
  Pus-pus-pus.
I got pushed by a platypus.

I bonked them with my boomerang.
I bonked them with my boomerang.
  Boomer, boomer,
  Rang-rang-rang.
  Boomer, boomer,
  Rang-rang-rang.
I bonked them with my boomerang.

They ran away to Bendigo.
They ran away to Bendigo.
  Bendi, Bendi,
  Go-go-go.
  Bendi, Bendi,
  Go-go-go.
They ran away to Bendigo.

Me-ow

Cat sat on the wall,
singing to the moon.
"Me-ow, me-ow, me-ow."

"Oh, that cat!"
said the man.
"I can't get to sleep."

He threw his boots
out of the window
at the cat.

But Cat went on singing.
"Me-ow, me-ow, me-ow."

"Stop that!" shouted the man,
and he threw his clock.

But Cat went on singing
to the moon.
"Me-ow, me-ow, me-ow."

Out of the window
came a brush,
and a cup,
and a hot water bottle,
and some flowers.

Cat jumped off the wall.

"Good," said the man.
"Now I can get some sleep."

Cat went in to town.
He called all his brothers.

"Brothers," he said, "just out of town
is a wall where I sing.
A man likes my singing.
He likes it so much, he threw
me presents."

"Presents!" shouted the cats.
"Come on.   Let's go."

One hundred and one cats
ran out of town.

Moon, moon, oh beautiful moon!

One hundred and one cats
jumped up on the wall.

And soon,
one hundred and one cats
sang to the moon.
"Me-ow, me-ow, me-ow."

48